GW00536982

Marcel Proust
On Life, Love and Letters

Marcel Proust
On Life, Love and Letters

Chosen and Translated by
Ronald and Odette Cortie

Illustrated by
Feliks Topolski

Introduction by
D. J. Enright

Cecil Woolf – London

First published in 1988

Cecil Woolf Publishers, 1 Mornington Place, London NW1 7RP
Tel: 01-387 2394

British Library Cataloguing in Publication Data
Proust, Marcel, *1871-1922*
Marcel Proust on life, love and letters.
I. Title II. Cortie, Ronald III. Cortie, Odette
IV. Topolski, Feliks, *1907–* V. [À la recherche
du temps perdu.] *English. Selections.*
843′.912 [F]

ISBN 0–900821–78–7

To

the memory

of

ODETTE VICTORIA CORTIE

Contents

Introduction

It can hardly be of no consequence that Marcel Proust's father was a distinguished physician, who played a leading part in the campaign against cholera, and his mother an ardent lover of the arts. In *Remembrance of Things Past* scientific analysis and artistic creation coexist with seeming ease, the one correcting or modifying the other. While science looks for general laws, every true work of art, Proust tells us, will reveal a unique accent, as if to demonstrate that 'in spite of the conclusions to which science seems to point, the individual did truly exist'.

Proust declared in a letter that his role as a novelist was analogous to that of Einstein. First came minute observation; then metaphorical transformation, exploration and evocation through images: Jupien as an orchid, Charlus as a 'providential' bumble-bee, then the two of them as a pair of birds in the early stages of courtship; and finally the considered judgement, the deduction of a general law. In this particular instance the watcher assumes the guise of a naturalist, prefacing the meeting between Charlus and Jupien at the beginning of *Cities of the Plain* with a short lecture on insects and the fertilization of flowers. Subsequent reflections have to do, immediately and comically, with the parity in respect of vociferousness between pain and pleasure, and then, more earnestly and at length, with the nervous mannerisms of the 'accursed' race of Sodom.

Though Proust has been praised for creating a novel out of highly original generalizations about human nature and conduct, for the most part we feel that the generalizations grow out of the fiction: at least, the fiction gives both definition and conviction to the general propositions. The extract on joking about subjects that embarrass us occurs in connection with the Duchesse de Guermantes's habit of carrying an umbrella. Should it begin to rain when she was some distance from home, she explains jokingly, a cabman might demand a fee 'beyond my means': the narrator surmises that she is recalling a time when she was relatively short of money. The sonorous speech on neurotics and their great achievements comes during a wryly amusing scene in *The Guermantes Way* in which Dr du Boulbon tries to comfort the narrator's grandmother by relating how, in a home for neurasthenics, he met a man who stood transfixed on a bench, not daring to turn his painfully bent neck for fear of catching a chill: 'That poor madman is the loftiest intellect I know.' The grandmother ought to be happy to belong to the 'splendid and pitiable family which is the salt of the earth'; in fact she is suffering from uraemia.

If excerption requires a precedent, it finds one close at hand in the notebook into which Mme Proust copied quotations from her favourite authors, passages testifying to a taste for general statements, to subtlety of mind, and (André Maurois has remarked) to a certain melancholic resignation. In excerption something of the power imparted by the context – the clarity and the persuasiveness – is inevitably lost, yet readers familiar with the novel will be able to supply the context from memory, and readers new to Proust may be induced to seek it.

The 'scientific' coolness of these Proustisms, as we might call them with his 'Bergottisms' in mind, is offset by the sufferings and less commonly the joys which Proust's characters experience in the service, as it may seem, of adducing the observations and bringing them alive. It is this that exempts him from the objection implied by one of the extracts included here: that 'a work of art containing theories is like a an object on which the price tag has been left'. The precision of his accounts of people and places deters any suspicion of the merely theoretical. When he was to speak of a painting, he would bestir himself and travel considerable distances to examine the painting in question. Details had to be absolutely correct, and he would ask astonished ladies of his acquaintance to show him hats or dresses they had worn twenty years earlier.

He recorded the words and phrases used by particular persons, and a jotting in his notebooks reads: '*ref* Tansonville – ask Monsieur Mâle whether the monks wore golden vestments at Christmas and Easter'. Sarah Bernhardt and Réjane were drawn on for the fictional actress, Berma, while Franck, Debussy and Saint-Saëns. among others, contributed to the figure of Vinteuil. Advice on musical matters was sought from musicians, on flowers from botanists, on medical matters from medical men. Virginia Woolf has noted that a couple of volumes about disease are scattered through his pages. In this insistence on exactness and factuality Proust resembles Thomas Mann, another master of the monumental and the meticulous, who also knew that if you are to engage in the metaphysical, the universal, and the abstract, you must base yourself on a sound, impeccable flooring of the actual, the physical, and the individual.

That art and memory loom large in the present compilation is only to be expected. And it is perfectly in proportion that there should be much about love, for Proust held that authors, whether ancient or modern, had never investigated the subject fully. 'Nothing is further removed from love than the ideas we entertain concerning it.' That his findings, the 'laws' he infers, are – to put it mildly – on the pessimistic side is probably because in this sphere, preeminently, investigation is unlikely to be exhaustive and all-embracing, rather than (as has been suggested) because Proust's own love was homosexual and hence abnormally 'difficult' or painful. (Also, Proust emphasizes, unhappiness is more fruitful for the writer than happiness: ideas come to him 'as the successors to griefs'.) To ascribe to his homosexuality the reference to adultery introducing the spirit into the letter which marriage tends to leave dead would be easy, but totally mistaken. Far from boring him, women fascinated him, and not merely as prudent substitutes for men. Much of *Cities of the Plain* could have come from a dyed-in-the-wool heterosexual.

The remark about adultery, with its biblical allusion to the spirit of the law and the letter, comes during a complex inquiry into the way 'unconsecrated unions' can none the less establish strong bonds of kinship (see the excerpt, Relationships, on page 46), while the inquiry itself arises out of Mlle Vinteuil's lesbian relationship with a woman who succeeds in deciphering Vinteuil's seemingly illegible annotations and thus ensures his fame as a composer.

The passages selected by Odette and Ronald Cortie are in no sense esoteric, or peculiar to the characters and events of the novel or its time and place. On the contrary, they are lucid, immediate in impact, and indeed, we may tell ourselves after the shock of recognition, they are what we ourselves have often thought, or suspected, but never managed to express so well. Here and there we find ourselves acknowledging the force of one particular generalization cited here: 'All readers read themselves . . .'

By way of tempering the occasionally repellent harshness and the dogmatic tone of some of these dicta, it seems appropriate to quote one of Proust's most affecting and affectionate passages, occurring in the narrator's meditations after the death of Bergotte, his fictional writer: a notably tentative passage, moreover, which allows of unknown laws. Neither spiritualism nor orthodox religion affords proof that the soul survives, yet is Bergotte permanently dead? Who can tell?

> We can only say that everything in this life is arranged as though we entered it carrying a

burden of obligations incurred in a former life; there is no intrinsic reason in the conditions of earthly life why we should suppose ourselves constrained to do good, to be considerate, or even polite, or why an atheistic artist should deem himself bound to begin over and over again, a score of times, a piece of work the admiration prompted by which will matter little to his worm-eaten body . . . All these obligations, which do not have their sanction in our present life, seem to belong to a different world, founded on kindness, scrupulousness and sacrifice, a world – wholly different from the present one —which we leave in order to be born on this earth, before perhaps returning there to to live again beneath the sovereignty of those unknown laws which we have obeyed because we bore their teaching in our hearts, without knowing whose hand had inscribed them there — those laws to which every profound work of the intellect brings us closer and which are invisible only—not quite only—to fools.

D.J. Enright

On Life

The superscript number printed after each quotation refers to the source, which is given in the Index at the end of the book.

On Life

REALITY

Reality is something which has no link with feasibility.[1]

CLOTHES

In the life of most women everything, even the deepest sadness, leads to a dressmaker's fitting.[2]

SNOBBERY

Snobbery is a serious illness of the spirit, but one that is localized and does not corrupt it as a whole.[3]

ELEGANCE AND THE INTELLECT

The intellectual qualities of a social gathering are generally in inverse, rather than direct ratio, to its elegance.[4]

ECCENTRICITIES

In order to make reality endurable we are obliged to encourage in ourselves a few small eccentricities.[5]

SORROW

Happiness is healthy for the body, but it is grief that develops the intellect.[6]

EXITS AND ENTRANCES

Every person is destroyed on vanishing from our sight; then his next appearance is a new creation different from the preceding one, if not from all others.[7]

JOKES

The things about which we most often joke are usually, on the contrary, the things that embarrass us. However, we have no desire to appear to be embarrassed by them, and entertain perhaps a secret hope of the added advantage that the person to whom we are talking, hearing us treat the matter as a jest, will assume that it is not true.[8]

AMBITION

We are always ready to despise an objective which we have not succeeded in reaching, or which we have permanently achieved.[9]

BOREDOM

Boredom is one of the least serious misfortunes we have to endure.[10]

SOCIAL CLASS

Each social class has its own pathology.[11]

OLD MEN

It is from adolescents who live long enough that life makes its old men.[12]

MORALITY

Moral duty is less clearly essential than our ethics teach us. Whatever the theosophical cafés and the Kantian pubs suggest, we are deplorably ignorant of the nature of good.[13]

SIMPLICITY

To be a great lady is to act the great lady; meaning, for one thing, to cultivate a simple manner. This is not easy, as simplicity delights only when others realize that you have no need to be simple.[14]

SEPARATION

In the same way in which it cools enmities, a long separation often reawakens friendships.[15]

TIME

In theory, we know that the earth turns even though we are unaware of this fact; the ground on which we walk does not appear to move, therefore we do not worry. In life the same may be said of time.[16]

LINKS

We are linked with others by the thousands of roots and threads made up from the memory of the preceding evening and our hopes for the following morning; an endless web from which we can never disengage ourselves.[17]

MORALITY

We become moral when we are unhappy.[18]

THE UNIVERSE

The universe is true for all of us and different for each of us.[19]

GENEROSITY

Generosity is often the front assumed by our egotistical desires before we have named and classified them.[20]

PLAGIARISM

The plagiarism that is most difficult for us to avoid is the plagiarism of ourselves.[21]

WELL-BEING

Our feeling good results less from our state of health than from the unused excess of our vitality, therefore we can achieve it just as easily by limiting our activity as by increasing our energy.[22]

DISCOVERIES

Beyond a certain age our memories are so inter-twined that our thoughts or the book that we are reading are of little importance. We have involved ourselves in everything, everything is productive, everything is dangerous; and the valuable discoveries that we make in Pascal's *Pensées* may equally well be inspired by an advertisement for soap.[23]

THE GENERATION GAP

For each individual the old regime is that of which we witnessed only the end. What we perceive on the horizon assumes a secretive nobility and seems to be the golden cadence of a whole world. Meanwhile we move on and soon we ourselves stand on the following generation's horizon; then once again the horizon recedes and the world that seemed finished begins again.[24]

SURPRISE

The world was not created once and for all for each of us. Throughout life things that we never even imagined are added to it.[25]

LACK OF IMAGINATION

Often a lack of imagination prevents onc from suffering as one might.[26]

FALSE ASSURANCE

Errors and ineptness do not diminish assurance. Quite the contrary.[27]

DEATH

We say that the hour of death cannot be forecast, but when we say this we imagine that hour as placed in an obscure and distant future. It never occurs to us that it has any connection with the day already begun or that death could arrive this same afternoon, this afternoon which is so certain and which has every hour filled in advance.[28]

REMEMBRANCE OF THINGS PAST

The idea of time is of value – and a spur – at moments of perception. And this life we experience in semi-darkness can be illuminated and this life that we continually distort can be restored to its true pristine shape. In short, a life can be realized through the confines of a book! How happy would be the man who had the power to write such a book! What a task awaited him![29]

WEATHER

A change in the weather is sufficient to recreate the world and ourselves.[30]

THE UNKNOWN

We are attracted by any form of life which represents something unknown, by a last illusion still unshattered.[31]

THE WORLD

The whole world is merely a vast sundial, a single lighted segment of which enables us to tell the time.[32]

GROWING UP

Once youth is past, a man usually frees himself from arrogance. He discovers that there are such things as literature and music, even standing for Parliament.[33]

DECEPTION

When has there not been some man high in public life, seen as a saint by his friends, who is found to have forged documents, robbed the state, betrayed his country?[34]

AGELESS

Man is a creature without a defined age who has the ability of becoming, in a few seconds, several years younger and, surrounded by the walls of time through which he has lived, floats between them as though in a bowl of water, the level of which is always changing, thus moving him into the range of this epoch and then of that.[35]

POSSIBILITIES

Consider the richness of the world of possibilities in comparison with the real world.[36]

PROBLEMS

Perhaps it is only people who lead really deprived lives who can be haunted by moral problems.[37]

CIVILIZATION

The progress of civilization permits each of us to reveal unsuspected graces and vices which make him more venerated by or more unbearable to his friends.[38]

THE FUTURE

Just as it is not the desire to become famous but the habit of working that enables us to produce a finished book, so it is not the activity of the present moment but wise reflections from the past that enable us to protect the future.[39]

AWARENESS

We scarcely make the most of our life, for during summer twilights or snowy winter nights we allow to pass, unappreciated, the hours which promised a little calmness or pleasure. Those hours are not completely lost, however. Later, when fresh moments of pleasure occur, which would normally drift away leaving the same feeble impression, the earlier ones provide them with a foundation, the texture of a rich orchestration.[40]

TOLERANCE

Certain fine qualities in us help us to be tolerant of another's faults; and a man of great talent generally pays less attention to another's stupidity than a fool would.[41]

INHERITED TRAITS

It is common knowledge that a child takes after both its father and its mother. Yet the sharing of the merits and defects which it inherits is so peculiarly planned that, of two fine qualities which seemed to be indivisible in one of the parents, you will observe only one in the child, and joined to that very fault in the other parent which seemed most mismatched with it.[42]

NEUROTICS

Despite popular opinion, neurotic people are perhaps the least likely of all of us to take notice of their presentiments: they hear so many things within themselves which they eventually realize should never have scared them that finally they pay attention to none. Their nervous system has so often cried 'Help! Help!' as if for a grave illness when only a snowstorm was about to begin, or a move to another flat, that they get into the habit of ignoring such warnings.[43]

OTHER MEN'S MOTIVES

Chemists have the power of analysis; sick men suffering from an unknown illness can send for the doctor; criminal mysteries are more or less solved by the examining magistrates. But when the disconcerting behaviour of our fellow men is in question, we rarely discover their motives.[44]

IMAGINATION

Life holds very little interest except on those days when the dust of reality is mixed with magic sand; when some mundane occurrence of daily life becomes a noble adventure. Then a complete vision of an inaccessible country emerges from the mists of the imagination and enters our life and, like the awakened sleeper, we see those persons of whom we had dreamed so passionately and whom we were convinced we would never see except in dreams.[45]

NO REGRETS

One way of becoming reconciled to life is to satisfy ourselves that the things and people that appear to be beautiful and mysterious from afar are, in fact, without beauty or mystery. This method is perhaps not the best one to choose, yet it does give us a certain equanimity that assists us through life and resigns us to death since, by assuring us that we have known the best and that the best was not much, it enables us to have no regrets.[46]

EGOTISTS

Egotists always have the final word; having made clear that their minds cannot be changed, the more one appeals to their finer feelings the more they rebuke, not themselves for having to prove themselves right, but those who place them in a position of having to prove themselves right.[47]

DISAPPOINTMENT

A cathedral, a wave in a tempest, the leap of a ballet dancer, never turn out to be as high as we had hoped.[48]

LEARNING

Our intellect is not the most subtle, the most powerful, the most appropriate, instrument for revealing the truth. It is life that, little by little, example by example, permits us to see that what is most important to our heart, or to our mind, is learned not by reasoning but through other agencies. Then it is that the intellect, observing their superiority, abdicates its control to them upon reasoned grounds and agrees to become their collaborator and lackey.[49]

REALITY

Even from a realistic point of view the countries we crave for play, at any given moment, a larger part in our real life than the country in which we are living.[50]

CHARACTER

The character that we project in the second part of our life is not always our original character developed or dried up, bloated or thinned out; often it is the reverse, like a suit turned inside out.[51]

DOCTORS

For each illness that doctors cure with medicine, they provoke ten in healthy people by inoculating them with the virus that is a thousand times more powerful than any microbe: the idea that one is ill.[52]

ADOLESCENCE

The particular feature of adolescence—a very fruitful rather than an ungrateful period—is that the less likeable characteristics of people seem to be an inseparable part of their personality. Surrounded by monsters and gods we experience no calm. There is scarcely one of our gestures of that period which we would not prefer now to forget. But what we must regret, on the contrary, is the loss of that spontaneity which produced those gestures. Later on in life we see things in a more practical fashion, in conformity with the rest of society, nevertheless adolescence is the only period during which we really learn things.[53]

RESIGNATION

Resignation, by moderating our habits, allows certain elements of our strength to be indefinitely increased.[54]

SOCIETY

There is published every day in Paris society, Balzac would tell us, a kind of spoken newspaper, more deadly than its printed rivals.[55]

MIRACLES

When we find ourselves on the brink of the abyss, and it appears that God has forsaken us, we do not hesitate to expect a miracle of Him.[56]

INSTINCT

A certain instinct resides in our body for what is good for us, just as our heart contains an instinctive sense of moral duty. And no authorization from a doctor of medicine or theology can replace these instincts. We know that cold baths are bad for us but we enjoy them; we can always find a doctor to prescribe them but not to prevent them from harming us.[57]

APPRECIATION

When sickness, a duel, or a runaway horse brings death near to us, we sense that we would have richly enjoyed life, the pleasures of the flesh, and unknown countries . . . all about to be taken from us. Yet once the danger has passed, we return to the same humdrum life in which none of these things existed.[58]

MISFORTUNES

There are moments in life when a kind of beauty is born from the many misfortunes that besiege us, intertwined like Wagnerian themes.[59]

DECISION

Only a state of mind that will not last causes us to make definitive resolutions.[60]

CHANGE

The greatest cause of suffering in life is when our heart changes. But we realize this sadness only in literature, only through the imagination. In reality our heart changes so slowly that, even if we are aware of each successive stage, the feeling of change is spared us.[61]

SICKNESS

In sickness we realize that, far from being alone, we live chained to, although worlds apart from, a creature totally different who does not know us and with whom it is impossible to communicate: our body. Should we meet a robber on the road, we might perhaps make him aware of his own peril and persuade him to take pity on us. But to ask pity of our body is to converse with an octopus, for whom our words can have no more meaning than the sound of water, and with which we would be horrified to be condemned to live.[62]

INVALIDS

Certain neurotics, from having initially pretended to be ill, end by becoming chronic invalids.[63]

PAIN

Illness is the most listened to of doctors: to goodness and wisdom we only make promises, but we obey pain.[64]

MIXED INTERESTS

The interests of our life are so mixed that often the preparations for a future happiness, as yet unknown, coincide with the aggravation of a sorrow from which we are now suffering.[65]

PEACE OF MIND

Since sadness is akin to sexual desire in that we intensify it by agitating about it, being very busy should engender not only chastity but also peace of mind.[66]

MEMORY

We quickly forget whatever we have not considered profoundly, whatever is produced by imitation or the passion of the moment will change, thus modifying our memory. Even more than diplomats, politicians fail to remember the point of view that they lately held, and some of their recantations stem less from an excess of ambition than from a failing memory. As for socialites they remember almost nothing.[67]

MEMORY AND CHANCE

We are able to find everything in our memory, which is like a dispensary or a chemical laboratory in which chance steers our hand sometimes to a soothing drug and sometimes to a dangerous poison.[68]

RECALL

What most effectively recalls a person to us is precisely what we had forgotten; because of its insignificance it has kept its original force unaltered by our thought.[69]

POSSESSIVENESS

That a man clings only to what he possesses, and that he who used to throw money around when he so rarely had any now hoards what he is so richly supplied with, is undoubtedly a common enough phenomenon.[70]

MONEY

An uncle of her father had recently left nearly twenty-four million francs to the girl, which meant that the Faubourg Saint-Germain was beginning to take notice of her.[71]

EARNINGS

The idea that all money is the same is false. A fresh method of earning it brings a lustre to the coins which use has tarnished.[72]

HABIT

Our habits permit us, generally, even physically, to endure an existence which initially would seem impossible.[73]

ASSOCIATIONS

If we see again something we have looked at long ago it brings back to us, together with our past vision, all the imagery with which it was imbued. This is because objects, as soon as they have been perceived by us, enter within us, share our reveries or our feelings at that time and merge indissolubly with them. A name seen in a book we once read contains within its syllables the swift wind and the bright sun of the moment we first read it. In the slightest sensation transmitted by the humblest nourishment, the smell of coffee and milk, we recover that vague hope of fine weather which enticed us when day was dawning and the morning sky unsure.[74]

HABIT

Throughout our lives stultifying habit hides almost all the universe from us and, in complete darkness, beneath their unchanged labels, substitutes for the most dangerous or most intoxicating poisons in life something anodyne which brings no thrills.[75]

THE PAST

We labour in vain to evoke our past; all our intellectual efforts are futile. The past remains hidden beyond the reach of the mind, in some material object (in the sensation which the material object would induce in us). And chance only decides whether or not we encounter that object before we die.[76]

REMEMBERING

Days in the past cover little by little those that came before and are themselves buried beneath those than follow them. But each past day stays deposited in us, as in a vast library in which there are older books, some of which perhaps no one will ever ask to see. Yet should a day from the past rise—through the lucidity of subsequent epochs – to the surface and envelop us, then for a moment names resume their former aspect, and we our state of mind at the time, and we feel with a vague agony, which will not last long, the insoluble problems which caused us such suffering at the time.[77]

SELF-DECEPTION

The soldier is convinced that a space of time, capable of being infinitely prolonged, will be granted him before the bullet finds him, the thief before he is arrested, all men generally, before they have to die. This is the talisman which preserves people and sometimes peoples, not from danger but from the dread of danger, or more correctly from the belief in danger, which in certain instances allows them to brave it without their really needing to be brave.[78]

OLD AGE

Old age resembles death in that some regard it with indifference, not because they are more courageous than others but because they have less imagination.[79]

CHANGE

The mind can be influenced like a plant, like a cell, like a chemical element; the only requirement is a set of new circumstances or a new environment.[80]

LOST PARADISES

If a memory, owing to forgetfulness, is unable to liaise or forge any link between itself and the present; if it has remained in its own place, of its own date; if it has retained its distance, its isolation in the fold of a valley or on the peak of a mountain, it induces us suddenly to breathe an air new to us precisely because it is an air we have previously breathed, that purer air which poets have vainly tried to enthrone in paradise, and which offers that profound sense of renewal only because it has been breathed before, since the true paradises are paradises we have lost.[81]

DOCTORS AND ARTISTS

Artists and intelligent people must have suitable doctors who prescribe treatments and medicines that are specially adapted to them. The same treatment cannot possibly be the same for them as for any Tom, Dick or Harry. Nine-tenths of the ills from which intelligent people suffer arise from their intellect. They need a doctor who understands that disease. A doctor will make allowances for gastric and digestive troubles while not making any allowance for the effect of reading Shakespeare.[82]

OTHER PEOPLE'S FAULTS

It seems that, more than anything else, we notice our own weaknesses in other people. Thus a short-sighted person says of another, 'But he's as blind as a bat!' A consumptive doubts the pulmonary robustness of healthy people. A foul-smelling man insists that others stink. A cuckold sees cuckolds everywhere, a promiscuous woman promiscuous women and a snob snobs. Then, the invert detects and denounces inverts, and the tailor when asked out to dine passes judgement on the cloth of your coat before speaking a word . . . We assume that everyone else is blind. Each of us has a private god in attendance who assures him that his own defects are concealed from other people.[83]

DECEPTION

Deception is essential to humanity. It plays as great a part perhaps as the search for pleasure and is moreover controlled by that search. We lie in order to protect our pleasure or our honour, if the revealing of our pleasure stains our honour. We lie throughout our life, especially perhaps to those who love us. They alone make us fear for our pleasure and we desire their esteem.[84]

FACES

The features of our face are no more than gestures made permanent by force of habit. Nature, like the destruction of Pompeii, like the metamorphosis of a nymph into a tree, has frozen us in an accustomed movement.[85]

GREAT AND SMALL MINDS

The benevolent condescension of great minds has as a corollary the incomprehension and hostility of small minds.[86]

THE PAST

Life is persistently weaving fresh threads which link people with events and these threads are crossed and recrossed, doubled and redoubled, thus thickening the web, so that, between one point of our past and all the others, a rich network of memories leaves us an infinite variety of communicating paths to choose from.[87]

DEFECTS AND VIRTUES

The variety of our defects is no less astonishing than the similarity of our virtues.[88]

GUILT

It is often painful to endure the tears that we ourselves have caused.[89]

HABIT

The regularity of a habit is usually in direct proportion to its absurdity.[90]

RETROSPECT

We assess a person's vices only when he ceases to be capable of indulging in them.[91]

HALF-ALIVE

Most of the time we are only half-alive. Many of our faculties remain asleep because they rely on habit which can perform without them.[92]

On Love

SEX APPEAL

Because of a charming law of nature which exists even in the most sophisticated societies, we live in complete ignorance of whatever we love.[96]

THE POETRY OF LOVE

We must not forget the delicious mirage that love projects and which totally and exclusively envelops the beloved, nor that the 'mistake' a man makes in marrying his cook or the mistress of his best friend is usually the only poetic act he performs in his entire life.[97]

DANGEROUS WATERS

The conversation of a woman who is loved is like a soil beneath which are concealed dangerous waters. Behind her words is the constant awareness of the freezing cold of an invisible lake, whose perfidious dampness seeps through in many places.[98]

PRETTY WOMEN

Let us leave pretty women to men who lack imagination.[99]

UNDERSTANDING

We want to be understood because we desire to be loved and we desire to be loved because we love. The understanding of anyone other than the beloved is of no importance and their love a nuisance.[100]

On Love

THE COLLECTOR

Certainly it is more reasonable to devote one's life to women than to postage stamps, antique snuff-boxes or even to paintings and sculptures – providing that the example of such collections reminds us not to limit ourselves to one woman.[93]

TIES

Intimacy with a woman we love creates social ties which outlive our love and even the recollection of our love.[94]

ELOPEMENT

A union stemming from an elopement is less permanent than others, because the fear of not obtaining the woman or of having her escape us is all our love. Once taken from her husband, torn from the theatre, cured of the temptation to leave us, in fact severed from our emotion, she is almost nothing, and, so long desired, is soon abandoned by the very person who was so afraid she would abandon him.[95]

Feliks Topolski

LOVESICKNESS

Those who are not in love never understand how an intelligent man can be so unhappy because of a very ordinary woman. This is the same as expressing surprise that anyone should be stricken with cholera because of a germ as tiny as the comma bacillus.[101]

PHYSICAL PLEASURE

Beneath any deep physical pleasure there lies a permanent danger.[102]

SECONDARY EFFECTS

It is remarkable how much admiration for his good qualities a person induces in the relatives of anyone with whom he has had sexual relations. Physical love, unjustly underestimated, impels everyone to display any trace of kindness and unselfishness to such a degree that those nearest to the beloved are deeply impressed.[103]

BEAUTY

It has been said that beauty is a promise of happiness. Conversely the possibility of happiness can be the beginning of beauty.[104]

CONCEALMENT

What a profound significance small things assume when a woman we love conceals them from us.[105]

BRIEF ENCOUNTERS

The charms of the passing woman are generally in direct proportion to the swiftness of her passing.[106]

CONSUMMATION

Those who love and those whose desires are satisfied are not the same men.[107]

COMPETITION

By analysing our love affairs more deeply, we realize that often a woman attracts us because of the many men with whom we have to compete for her possession, and we suffer terribly in doing this; but eliminate the men and the woman's charm vanishes.[108]

ADULTERY

Adultery introduces the spirit into the letter which quite often marriage has left dead.[109]

DEFINITION OF LOVE

Love is space and time made apparent to the heart.[110]

LOSS AND GAIN

Perhaps only those who are capable of making us suffer deeply can, during the moments of respite, provide us with the same gentle calmness that nature dispenses.[111]

SUFFERING

For a woman to make one suffer deeply, one must have believed in her implicitly.[112]

SUFFERING AND POWER

Every new suffering that a woman, often unwittingly, inflicts upon us, increases her power over us and also our demands upon her.[113]

NEEDS

The woman we love seldom satisfies all our needs and we deceive her with a woman we do not love.[114]

THE BELOVED

The beloved is successively the illness and the cure that aggravates and suspends the illness.[115]

CHANGING THE BELOVED

We are sculptors modelling from a woman an entirely different statue from the one she presents to us.[116]

THE KEPT WOMAN

A woman whom we are keeping never seems to us a 'kept woman'.[117]

THE MISTRESS AS TEACHER

For many a young man of society who is uncultivated, awkward, without charm or taste, his mistress is his teacher and a love affair the only school in which he is initiated into the highest culture and learns the value of disinterested knowledge.[118]

REVELATION

Often we discover that we are in love—perhaps we even fall in love—only on the day of parting.[119]

YOUNG GIRLS

We believe that we are in love with a young girl, but we merely love in her, alas, that dawn whose blush her face fleetingly reflects.[120]

TRUTH AND LIES

The deception of proclaiming a truth while blending it with a barrage of lies is more prevalent than is generally thought.[121]

RELATIONSHIPS

Unconsecrated unions produce relationships that are just as numerous and as complicated as those created by marriage, but often more permanent.[122]

SEPARATION

In a separation it is the one who is not really in love who says the more tender things.[123]

JEALOUSY

With jealousy there is neither past nor future; what it imagines is always in the present.[124]

EVOLUTION OF LOVE

In the beginning love is fashioned by desire; later on it is kept alive by anxiety. In gnawing anxiety as in joyful desire love demands everything. It is born and lives only if something remains to be won. We love only what we do not totally possess.[125]

JEALOUS LOVERS

Jealousy is an intermittent malady, the cause of which is capricious, imperious, always identical in one patient, often completely different in another. We see a jealous lover who is jealous only of the men with whom his mistress has sexual relations at a distance, yet permits her to give herself to another man, if it is done with his permission, near at hand, if not performed before his eyes, under his roof. This situation is not uncommon among elderly men who are in love with young women. Such a man feels the difficulty of pleasing her, sometimes his inability to satisfy her, and, sooner than risk being deceived, prefers to admit to his house, to an adjoining room, some man whom he considers incapable of giving her bad advice, but not incapable of giving her pleasure.[126]

JEALOUSY AND DECEPTION

As soon as jealousy is discovered it is seen by the one who is the object of it as a suspicion which permits deception.[127]

JEALOUSY

The demon jealousy cannot be exorcised for it always returns in a new form.[128]

SICK DOUBTS

Jealousy belongs to that family of sick doubts which are resolved more definitely by the force of a protestation than by its plausibility. A characteristic of love is that it makes us, simultaneously, more suspicious and more credulous.[129]

ACCESSIBILITY

If the women from what used to be called the closed houses, and prostitutes, providing that we know them to be prostitutes, attract us so little, it is not that they are less attractive than other women, it is because they are ready and waiting, the object that we are seeking they offer us prepared; it is because they are not conquests.[130]

VOICES

Love helps us to discern things, to discriminate. Standing in a wood, the bird-lover instantly recognizes the notes of the various species. The lover of girls knows that human voices vary even more. Each possesses more notes than the richest musical instrument and the combinations in which the voice groups those notes are as inexhaustible as the infinite diversity of personalities.[131]

THE IRRATIONALITY OF LOVE

It is often said that by telling a friend of his mistress's shortcomings one succeeds only in making him love her even more, because he does not believe what he is told, yet how much truer this is if he does believe it![132]

DARKROOM

There are pleasures which resemble photographs. In the company of our beloved we get only a negative and we develop it later, on returning home, in that inner darkroom to which entrance is forbidden as long as we are among other people.[133]

A LUXURY

A woman is enchanted if, without yielding anything, she can receive more than she usually gets when she does give herself. Women understand and realize that they can afford the luxury of never yielding to those who from the beginning have betrayed their eternal desire.[134]

TWO FACES

Every lover, perhaps everyone, is like Janus to us, exposing the face we like when he or she leaves us and the other face when we know him or her to be constantly at our beck and call.[135]

TOUCHING INSTINCT

She used her hands so clumsily while eating that one assumed that she must appear extremely awkward upon the stage. She recovered her dexterity only when making love, with that touching instinct in women who love the male body so intensely that they at once divine what will give most pleasure to that body, which is so different from their own.[136]

A PARADOX

There is in woman something akin to the unconscious function of drugs which are cunning without knowing it, like morphine. They are not indispensable for those to whom they give the benison of sleep and well-being. It is not by such people that they will be purchased for their weight in gold, or in exchange, but by those unfortunates to whom the drug brings no slumber, yields no pleasure, but who, without it, are subject to an agitation which they must at all costs terminate, even though to do so results in death.[137]

BENEFITS OF ABSTENTION

A neurotic patient cannot believe the doctor who urges him to calm himself by staying in bed and not receiving letters or reading newspapers. He presumes that such a life would increase his nervous tension. A lover, living in a state of emotional agony, cannot believe in the beneficial effect of renunciation.[138]

WEAKNESS IN THE BELOVED

The clear perception of special weaknesses in those we love in no way diminishes our affection for them; in fact that affection makes us find those weaknesses charming.[139]

SENSUAL LOVE

Vaguely awaited, instinctive and hidden, it rises to a passionate climax only at the moment it realizes those other pleasures which we discover in the tender glances and kisses of the woman at our side, and it seems to us, above all else, a manifestation of our consideration and gratitude for our companion's kindness of heart, and for her touching concern for ourselves which we measure by the blessings and the happiness that she showers upon us.[140]

On Art

On Art

THE COSTS

All great works come from neurotics. They alone have founded our religions and created our masterpieces. The world will never know the debt that it owes them, nor the pain they have suffered while enriching us. We enjoy exquisite music, beautiful paintings, a thousand shades of thought, never realizing the cost to those who created them in sleepless nights, tears, wild laughter, skin eruptions, asthmas, epilepsies and the dread of death which is the worst of all.[141]

A SOLE BEAUTY

Great authors create but one work, or rather they consistently reflect through various media a sole beauty that they have brought into the world.[142]

CREATION

It is our passions which shape our books and intervals of calm which write them.[143]

A LIBRARY

A library is the finest place to meditate on the dream of life.[144]

BEAUTY AND UGLINESS

Beauty is a sequence of hypotheses which ugliness arrests and blocks the pathway that we perceived opening into the unknown.[145]

READING

Reading teaches us to take a more exalted view of the value of life, a value which at the time we did not appreciate, and of whose magnitude we have only become aware through the book.[146]

TALK AND CREATION

We may talk for a lifetime without doing more than repeat the nothingness of the moment, whereas the march of thought in the lonely labour of artistic creation advances downwards into the depths, in the only direction that is not barred to us, along which we are free to advance, with further effort, towards the goal of truth.[147]

LIFE IMITATING ART

At the time of Rasputin's murder, at a supper party à la Dostoevsky, people were impressed by its strong Russian flavour. For life deceives us so much that we eventually believe that literature has no relation to it and we are astounded that the splendid ideas that books have presented to us are freely exhibited in daily life, that, for example, a murder at a supper party, a Russian incident, should have a Russian flavour.[148]

Feliks Topolski

A NEW UNIVERSE

Experts tell us today that Renoir was a great eighteenth-century painter. But in saying that they forget the element of time and how much time it took, even in the late nineteenth century, before Renoir was recognized as an artist of genius. In order to gain such a reputation, the original painter or the original writer proceeds in the manner of an oculist. The course of treatment is not always pleasing to us. But when it is finished, the artist says to us: 'Now behold!' and suddenly the world (which was not created once and for all, but as often as an original artist has emerged) seems to us completely different yet perfectly clear. Women passing in the street are somehow different from those of yesterday; they are Renoir women, the same as those in the paintings, whom we refused to accept as women. The carriages are Renoirs, and the water and the sky. We wish to walk in a forest like the one which at first seemed to us anything but a forest – for example, a tapestry full of the subtlest shades of colour except those which belong to forests. Such is the new and perishable universe which has just been created. It will endure until the next geological catastrophe unleashed by a new original painter or writer.[149]

CRITICS

Each generation of critics does nothing except maintain the opposite of the truths accepted by their predecessors.[150]

TRUE ART

The greatness of true art is that it rediscovers, holds, and communicates to us that reality from which we live further and further away, as the conventional knowledge we substitute for it becomes heavier and more impenetrable.[151]

GENIUS

We are slow to recognize in the individual physiognomy of a new writer the model which in our portfolio of ideas we classify as 'great genius'. We speak of originality, charm, power and finesse; later on we realize that all this is exactly what we mean by genius.[152]

IMPRESSIONS

As the spectrum exteriorizes for us the composition of light, the harmony of a Wagner and the colour of a Manet permit us to know the qualitative essence of another person's impressions.[153]

THE READER

All readers read themselves. The writer's work is a kind of optical instrument that enables the reader to discern what, without the book, he would never have seen in himself.[154]

THE ARTIST

To be totally true to his spiritual life an artist must remain solitary and not be prodigal of himself even to his followers.[155]

INSPIRATION

The immense change brought by the Great War was in inverse ratio to the value of the minds it touched, that is, up to a certain point; for, at the bottom, the fools and the voluptuaries were indifferent to the war, while those at the top who create their own world, their own inner life, are little concerned with the importance of events. What modifies their thought is something of no apparent significance which defeats the order of time and makes them live in another period of their lives. A bird singing in the Park of Montboissier, or a breeze heavy with the scent of mignonette, are clearly of less value than the mighty events of the Revolution and the Empire; nevertheless, they inspired in Chateaubriand's *Mémoires d'Outre-tombe* pages of far greater importance.[156]

ORIGINALITY

The public's knowledge of the charm, the graces and the formal aspects of nature is deduced from the patterns of a slowly assimilated art, and an original artist sets out by rejecting those patterns.[157]

STYLE

For a writer or for a painter, style is a matter not of technique but of vision. It is the revelation, which would be impossible by direct and conscious ways, of the qualitative difference between our diverse manners of seeing the world; a difference which, except for art, would eternally stay the secret of the individual.[158]

EFFORT

What we have not had to decipher and to analyse by our own effort, anything that was clear before we came, does not belong to us. Only what we extract from the obscurity within us truly belongs to us. And, since art rebuilds life exactly, surrounding these truths that we have discovered in ourselves floats an atmosphere of poetry, the sweetness of a mystery which is only the internal darkness we have traversed.[159]

THE TRUE LAST JUDGEMENT

It is instinct which dictates duty and the intelligence which offers reasons for avoiding it. But excuses do not exist in art; the artist must always pursue his instinct, which makes art the most real thing, the most austere school in life and the true last judgement.[160]

SEEKING OR CREATING?

There is a pit of uncertainty whenever the mind outdistances itself, when it is at the same time the explorer and the shadowy country to be explored, in which all our knowledge and qualifications will be of no avail. Are we seeking or creating? The mind is facing something that does not yet exist, to which it alone can give reality and illuminate with reason's light.[161]

CREATION

The state of mind in which one creates is well above the level of that in which one observes.[162]

THE MUSE OF HISTORY

The muse that has collected everything the higher muses of philosophy and art have rejected, all that is not based in truth, all that is fortuitous but which reveals other laws, is the Muse of History.[163]

UNDERSTANDING

Just as priests, possessing the widest experience of the human heart, are best qualified to pardon the sins which they do not themselves commit, so genius, having the widest experience of the human intelligence, can best understand the ideas most directly opposing those which form the foundation of its own writings.[164]

MEDIOCRITY

It made one think of those mediocre actors or novelists who, at certain periods, are hailed as men of genius, either because of the mediocrity of their contemporaries – among whom there is no artist with the ability to reveal genuine talent – or because of the ordinariness of the public, which, should there exist a unique individuality, would be incapable of understanding it.[165]

INTIMATIONS OF MORTALITY

Those who believe their creations to be enduring acquire the habit of contemplating their works in a later epoch when they themselves will be nothing but dust. And so, by compelling them to envisage the void, the thought of glory saddens them, for it is inseparable from the thought of death.[166]

UNIQUENESS OF THE ARTIST

The reason a work of genius is not easily understood and admired from the first is that the man who has created it is so extraordinary, that few other men resemble him. It was Beethoven's Twelfth, Thirteenth, Fourteenth and Fifteenth Quartets, played over a period of fifty years, that formed, educated and enlarged a public able to appreciate and understand Beethoven's Quartets.[167]

PARSIFAL

What the Good Friday music in *Parsifal* symbolized was a natural miracle which one could see performed by the spring every year, if one had the sense to find it, helped by the heady perfume of blossom.[168]

WAGNER

Consider how much of the real there is in the work of Wagner, notice in the mind's eye those insistent, fleeting themes which visit, withdraw, and then return, and, something far away, drowsy, almost detached, are at other moments, while remaining vague, so urgent and so near, so internal, organic, visceral, that one would call them the renewal not so much of a musical motif as of an attack of neuralgia.[169]

SPIRITUAL REALITY

The elevated and pure emotion that a piece of sculpture or a musical composition can invoke must surely correspond to a certain spiritual reality.[170]

ORIGINS

It is an impressive thought that the masterpieces which are perhaps the most extraordinary of our time have emerged not from the university degree, or from a model academic education on conventional lines, but from the persistent patronage of race-course paddocks and fashionable bars.[171]

THE AGEING ARTIST

He was approaching the age at which we rely upon bodily sensations to stimulate the forces of the brain. It is the age at which we like to caress beauty with our eyes objectively outside ourselves, to have it near us, in a tapestry, in a lovely sketch by Titian picked up in a second-hand shop, in a mistress as lovely as Titian's sketch.[172]

INDIVIDUALITY

The influence of local materials on the genius who uses them and extracts a particular characteristic from them does not make his work any less individual. Whether it be the work of an architect, a cabinet maker or a musician, it mirrors no less minutely the subtle aspects of the artist's personality because he has been required to work in Senlis millstone or the red sandstone of Strasbourg, because he has respected the knots peculiar to the ash, or because his score has recognized the resources and tonal limitations of the flute or the saxophone.[173]

ANTIQUITY

Associations of classical antiquity are one of the reasons for the pleasure a booklover derives from reading an Ode by Horace that is perhaps inferior to a modern poem which would leave the same reader cold.[174]

BERMA/BERNHARDT

Berma's acting demonstrated what was meant by nobility, by intelligence of diction. . . . But, at the same time, she made her words, her lines, even her whole speeches, flow into lakes of sound vaster than themselves, at the margins of which it was a joy to see them obliged to stop, to break off; thus does a poet take delight in holding back for a moment at the rhyming point the word which is about to leap forth, and a composer, merging the various words of his libretto in a single rhythm, contradicts, captures and controls them. So into the prose sentences of the modern playwright as into the poetry of Racine, Berma managed to introduce those expansive images of grief, nobility, passion, which were the masterpieces of her own personal art.[175]

LOST TIME

A work of art is the only means of regaining lost time. All the materials for a literary work are one's past experience, acquired in the midst of frivolous amusements, idleness, tenderness and pain, stored up without one divining their destination or their survival, for the seed possesses in reserve all the ingredients which will nourish and sustain the plant.[176]

THE LANGUAGE OF MUSIC

The andante had just concluded upon a phrase filled with tenderness. There followed before the next movement a short interval during which the musicians rested and the audience exchanged opinions. A duke, in order to demonstrate his knowledge, declared, 'It is difficult to perform well.' Other more entertaining people exchanged conversation. But what were their words, which like every human and external word left one so indifferent, compared to the heavenly phrase of music that had just been performed? And, just as certain animals are the final examples of a form of life which nature has abandoned, is not music the unique example of what – if the invention of language, the construction of words, the analysis of ideas had not intervened – might have been the means of communication? It is like a possibility that has ended in nothing: the human race has developed along other pathways, those of spoken and written language.[177]

MUSIC

The impression that these musical phrases of Vinteuil transmitted was different from any other, as though, in spite of the conclusions to which science seems to point, the individual did truly exist.[178]

WRITING

Writing is a sanitary and indispensable function for the writer and brings him satisfaction in much the same way as exercise, sweating and baths do for an athlete.[179]

LAST AND LONGEST

Great works of art do not begin by giving us all their best. In a new sonata the beauties one finds immediately are those of which one tires most quickly because, no doubt, they are less different from what one already knows. But when those first impressions have passed, there remains for our enjoyment a sequence whose structure, so original, strange and unique, is imperceptible to our mind and therefore preserved intact. And this sequence, which we had met every day without knowing it, which had been held in reserve for us and which, by the sheer force of its loveliness, had become invisible and unknown, this comes to us last of all. Consequently, this is the last we shall relinquish, for we shall love it longer than the rest because we have taken longer to learn to love it.[180]

CHALLENGE

The impression given to us by a person, or a work of art, or a performance for that matter, of marked individuality is special to that person or work and we bring to it the ideas of 'beauty', 'breadth of interpretation', 'pathos', etc. which we might, failing anything better, have had the illusion of perceiving in the run-of-the-mill show of a conventional face or talent, but our critical spirit has before it the insistent challenge of a form of which it possesses no intellectual equivalent, in which it must detect and single out the unknown element.[181]

ORIGINALITY

Artistic originality demands the elimination of the current fashions to which we were accustomed and which seemed reality itself. Therefore any new style of speaking, as well as new painting and new music, seems artificial and fatiguing, for it is founded on ways of speech which are unfamiliar, and the speaker appears to talk exclusively in metaphors.[182]

Source Index

La Duchesse de Guermantes
Morel

Topolski

Monsieur de Charlus

Feliks

Source Index

The text of *À la Recherche du Temps Perdu* from which the preceding excerpts are drawn is the fifteen-volume collected edition published by *NRF*, Librairie Gallimard (1923-27). Each quotation is numbered and below are given the abbreviated title, volume number in brackets, and page reference, followed by the reference to the twelve-volume English translation by C.K. Scott Moncrieff/ Andreas Mayor (Chatto & Windus, 1922-30/70).

ABBREVIATIONS

CS	*Du Côté de chez Swann* (2 vols)	
JFF	*À l'Ombre des Jeunes Filles en Fleur* (2 vols)	
CG	*Le Côté de Guermantes* (1) (1 vol.)	
CG	*Le Côté de Guermantes* (2)	(1 vol.)
SG	*Sodome et Gomorrhe* (1)	
SG	*Sodome et Gomorrhe* (2) (3 vols)	
LP	*La Prisonnière* (2 vols)	
AD	*Albertine Disparue* (2 vols)	
LTR	*Le Temps Retrouvé* (2 vols)	

SW	*Swann's Way* (2 vols)
BG	*Within a Budding Grove* (2 vols)
GW	*The Guermantes Way* (2 vols)
COP	*Cities of the Plain* (2 vols)
CVE	*The Captive* (2 vols)
SCG	*The Sweet Cheat Gone* (1 vol.)
TR	*Time Regained* (1 vol.)

INDEX